I
DERSERVE
Journal

A journal to assist in creating the
mindset that you deserve

LaCresha
Cunningham,
LCSW

For Information, Contact:
Email address: lcunni@healingsacredscars.com
Website: www.healingsacredscars.com

I Deserve Journal
ISBN 979-8-9874846-1-6
Printed in The United States of America

Morning Gratitude

Date: _____

Today I deserve to feel...

_____
_____
_____

Today I will give love to myself by...

_____
_____
_____

3 things I'm grateful for today are...

_____
_____
_____

"Happiness is a habit."

You are my MAGIC

Things I'm proud of achieving today are...

_____
_____
_____
_____
_____
_____
_____
_____
_____
_____
_____
_____
_____
_____
_____
_____
_____
_____

"Believe. You're halfway there."

Things I feel today that I choose to release and leave here...

_____
_____
_____
_____
_____
_____
_____
_____
_____
_____
_____
_____
_____
_____
_____
_____

"Believe. You're halfway there."

5 minute journaling

Date:

_____

_____

_____

_____

_____

_____

_____

_____

_____

_____

_____

_____

_____

_____

_____

_____

_____

_____

You Create

the Life You Deserve

Morning Gratitude

Date: _____

Today I deserve to feel...

_____
_____
_____

Today I will give love to myself by...

_____
_____
_____

3 things I'm grateful for today are...

_____
_____
_____

"Happiness is a habit."

Things I'm proud of achieving today are...

_____
_____
_____
_____
_____
_____
_____
_____
_____
_____
_____
_____
_____
_____
_____
_____
_____

"Believe. You're halfway there."

Things I feel today that I choose to release and leave here...

_____

_____

_____

_____

_____

_____

_____

_____

_____

_____

_____

_____

_____

_____

_____

"Believe. You're halfway there."

5 minute journaling

Date:

_____

_____

_____

_____

_____

_____

_____

_____

_____

_____

_____

_____

_____

_____

_____

_____

_____

_____

_____

_____

You Create
the Life You Deserve

Morning Gratitude

Date: _____

Today I deserve to feel...

_____
_____
_____

Today I will give love to myself by...

_____
_____
_____

3 things I'm grateful for today are...

_____
_____
_____

"Happiness is a habit."

You are my MAGIC

Things I'm proud of achieving today are...

_____
_____
_____
_____
_____
_____
_____
_____
_____
_____
_____
_____
_____
_____
_____
_____
_____

"Believe. You're halfway there."

Things I feel today that I choose to release and leave here...

_____

_____

_____

_____

_____

_____

_____

_____

_____

_____

_____

_____

_____

_____

_____

_____

"Believe. You're halfway there."

5 minute journaling

Date:

_____

_____

_____

_____

_____

_____

_____

_____

_____

_____

_____

_____

_____

_____

_____

_____

_____

_____

_____

_____

You Create
the Life You Deserve

Morning Gratitude

Date: _____

Today I deserve to feel...

_____
_____
_____

Today I will give love to myself by...

_____
_____
_____

3 things I'm grateful for today are...

_____
_____
_____

"Happiness is a habit."

You are my
MAGIC

Things I'm proud of achieving today are...

_____
_____
_____
_____
_____
_____
_____
_____
_____
_____
_____
_____
_____
_____
_____
_____
_____

"Believe. You're halfway there."

Things I feel today that I choose to release and leave here...

_____
_____
_____
_____
_____
_____
_____
_____
_____
_____
_____
_____
_____
_____
_____
_____
_____

"Believe. You're halfway there."

5 minute journaling

Date:

_____

_____

_____

_____

_____

_____

_____

_____

_____

_____

_____

_____

_____

_____

_____

_____

_____

_____

_____

You Create
the Life You Deserve

Morning Gratitude

Date: _____

Today I deserve to feel...

_____
_____
_____

Today I will give love to myself by...

_____
_____
_____

3 things I'm grateful for today are...

_____
_____
_____

"Happiness is a habit."

You are my
MAGIC

Things I'm proud of achieving today are...

_____
_____
_____
_____
_____
_____
_____
_____
_____
_____
_____
_____
_____
_____
_____
_____
_____

"Believe. You're halfway there."

Things I feel today that I choose to release and leave here...

_____
_____
_____
_____
_____
_____
_____
_____
_____
_____
_____
_____
_____
_____
_____
_____

"Believe. You're halfway there."

5 minute journaling   Date:

You Create
the Life
You Deserve

Morning Gratitude

Date: _____

Today I deserve to feel...

_____
_____
_____

Today I will give love to myself by...

_____
_____
_____

3 things I'm grateful for today are...

_____
_____
_____

"Happiness is a habit."

Things I'm proud of achieving today are...

_____
_____
_____
_____
_____
_____
_____
_____
_____
_____
_____
_____
_____
_____
_____
_____

"Believe. You're halfway there."

Things I feel today that I choose to release and leave here...

_____
_____
_____
_____
_____
_____
_____
_____
_____
_____
_____
_____
_____
_____
_____
_____
_____
_____

"Believe. You're halfway there."

5 minute journaling

Date:

_____

_____

_____

_____

_____

_____

_____

_____

_____

_____

_____

_____

_____

_____

_____

_____

_____

_____

_____

_____

You Create
the Life
You Deserve

Morning Gratitude

Date: _____

Today I deserve to feel...

_____

_____

_____

Today I will give love to myself by...

_____

_____

_____

3 things I'm grateful for today are...

_____

_____

_____

"Happiness is a habit."

You are my MAGIC

Things I'm proud of achieving today are...

_____
_____
_____
_____
_____
_____
_____
_____
_____
_____
_____
_____
_____
_____
_____
_____

"Believe. You're halfway there."

Things I feel today that I choose to release and leave here...

_____
_____
_____
_____
_____
_____
_____
_____
_____
_____
_____
_____
_____
_____
_____
_____
_____
_____

"Believe. You're halfway there."

5 minute journaling

Date:

_____

_____

_____

_____

_____

_____

_____

_____

_____

_____

_____

_____

_____

_____

_____

_____

_____

You Create
the Life
You Deserve

Morning Gratitude

Date: _____

Today I deserve to feel...

_____

_____

_____

Today I will give love to myself by...

_____

_____

_____

3 things I'm grateful for today are...

_____

_____

_____

"Happiness is a habit."

You are my MAGIC

Things I'm proud of achieving today are...

_____

_____

_____

_____

_____

_____

_____

_____

_____

_____

_____

_____

_____

_____

_____

_____

_____

"Believe. You're halfway there."

Things I feel today that I choose to release and leave here...

_____

_____

_____

_____

_____

_____

_____

_____

_____

_____

_____

_____

_____

_____

_____

_____

"Believe. You're halfway there."

5 minute journaling

Date:

_____

_____

_____

_____

_____

_____

_____

_____

_____

_____

_____

_____

_____

_____

_____

_____

_____

_____

_____

You Create
the Life
You Deserve

Weekly check in

DATE _____

TOP 3 THINGS I DID THIS WEEK
- _____
- _____
- _____

THIS WEEK I FELT

NEXT WEEK I WANT TO
_____
_____
_____
_____

MOST REWARDING INTERACTION I HAD THIS WEEK

THINGS I ACCOMPLISHED THIS WEEK

WHAT WAS THE BEST THING ABOUT THE WEEK?

MY RANKING OF THE WEEK
☆ ☆ ☆ ☆ ☆

Morning Gratitude

Date: _____

Today I deserve to feel...

_____
_____
_____

Today I will give love to myself by...

_____
_____
_____

3 things I'm grateful for today are...

_____
_____
_____

"Happiness is a habit."

You are my MAGIC

Things I'm proud of achieving today are...

_____
_____
_____
_____
_____
_____
_____
_____
_____
_____
_____
_____
_____
_____
_____
_____
_____

"Believe. You're halfway there."

Things I feel today that I choose to release and leave here...

_____
_____
_____
_____
_____
_____
_____
_____
_____
_____
_____
_____
_____
_____
_____
_____
_____

"Believe. You're halfway there."

5 minute journaling

Date:

_____

_____

_____

_____

_____

_____

_____

_____

_____

_____

_____

_____

_____

_____

_____

_____

_____

_____

You Create
the Life
You Deserve

Morning Gratitude

Date: _____

Today I deserve to feel...

_____
_____
_____

Today I will give love to myself by...

_____
_____
_____

3 things I'm grateful for today are...

_____
_____
_____

"Happiness is a habit."

You
are my
MAGIC

Things I'm proud of achieving today are...

_____
_____
_____
_____
_____
_____
_____
_____
_____
_____
_____
_____
_____
_____
_____
_____
_____

"Believe. You're halfway there."

Things I feel today that I choose to release and leave here...

_____
_____
_____
_____
_____
_____
_____
_____
_____
_____
_____
_____
_____
_____
_____
_____
_____
_____

"Believe. You're halfway there."

5 minute journaling   Date:

_____

_____

_____

_____

_____

_____

_____

_____

_____

_____

_____

_____

_____

_____

_____

_____

_____

_____

You Create
the Life
You Deserve

Morning Gratitude

Date: _____

Today I deserve to feel...

_____
_____
_____

Today I will give love to myself by...

_____
_____
_____

3 things I'm grateful for today are...

_____
_____
_____

"Happiness is a habit."

Things I'm proud of achieving today are...

_____
_____
_____
_____
_____
_____
_____
_____
_____
_____
_____
_____
_____
_____
_____
_____

"Believe. You're halfway there."

Things I feel today that I choose to release and leave here...

_____
_____
_____
_____
_____
_____
_____
_____
_____
_____
_____
_____
_____
_____
_____
_____
_____

"Believe. You're halfway there."

5 minute journaling

Date:

_____

_____

_____

_____

_____

_____

_____

_____

_____

_____

_____

_____

_____

_____

_____

_____

_____

_____

_____

You Create
the Life
You Deserve

Morning Gratitude

Date: _____

Today I deserve to feel...

_____
_____
_____

Today I will give love to myself by...

_____
_____
_____

3 things I'm grateful for today are...

_____
_____
_____

"Happiness is a habit."

Things I'm proud of achieving today are...

_____

_____

_____

_____

_____

_____

_____

_____

_____

_____

_____

_____

_____

_____

_____

_____

"Believe. You're halfway there."

Things I feel today that I choose to release and leave here...

_____

_____

_____

_____

_____

_____

_____

_____

_____

_____

_____

_____

_____

_____

_____

_____

"Believe. You're halfway there."

5 minute journaling

Date:

_____

_____

_____

_____

_____

_____

_____

_____

_____

_____

_____

_____

_____

_____

_____

_____

_____

_____

You Create
the Life
You Deserve

Morning Gratitude

Date: _____

Today I deserve to feel...

_____

_____

_____

Today I will give love to myself by...

_____

_____

_____

3 things I'm grateful for today are...

_____

_____

_____

"Happiness is a habit."

You are my MAGIC

Things I'm proud of achieving today are...

_____
_____
_____
_____
_____
_____
_____
_____
_____
_____
_____
_____
_____
_____
_____
_____
_____
_____
_____

"Believe. You're halfway there."

Things I feel today that I choose to release and leave here...

_____

_____

_____

_____

_____

_____

_____

_____

_____

_____

_____

_____

_____

_____

_____

_____

_____

_____

"Believe. You're halfway there."

5 minute journaling

Date:

You Create
the Life
You Deserve

Morning Gratitude

Date: _____

Today I deserve to feel...

_____

_____

_____

Today I will give love to myself by...

_____

_____

_____

3 things I'm grateful for today are...

_____

_____

_____

"Happiness is a habit."

You are my

MAGIC

Things I'm proud of achieving today are...

_____

_____

_____

_____

_____

_____

_____

_____

_____

_____

_____

_____

_____

_____

_____

_____

_____

_____

"Believe. You're halfway there."

Things I feel today that I choose to release and leave here...

_____
_____
_____
_____
_____
_____
_____
_____
_____
_____
_____
_____
_____
_____
_____
_____

"Believe. You're halfway there."

5 minute journaling

Date:

_____

_____

_____

_____

_____

_____

_____

_____

_____

_____

_____

_____

_____

_____

_____

_____

_____

_____

You Create
the Life
You Deserve

Morning Gratitude

Date: _____

Today I deserve to feel...

_____
_____
_____

Today I will give love to myself by...

_____
_____
_____

3 things I'm grateful for today are...

_____
_____
_____

"Happiness is a habit."

You are my

MAGIC

Things I'm proud of achieving today are...

_____
_____
_____
_____
_____
_____
_____
_____
_____
_____
_____
_____
_____
_____
_____
_____
_____
_____

"Believe. You're halfway there."

Things I feel today that I choose to release and leave here...

_____

_____

_____

_____

_____

_____

_____

_____

_____

_____

_____

_____

_____

_____

_____

_____

_____

"Believe. You're halfway there."

5 minute journaling   ♥   Date:

_____

_____

_____

_____

_____

_____

_____

_____

_____

_____

_____

_____

_____

_____

_____

_____

_____

_____

You Create
the Life
You Deserve

Morning Gratitude

Date: _____

Today I deserve to feel...

_____
_____
_____

Today I will give love to myself by...

_____
_____
_____

3 things I'm grateful for today are...

_____
_____
_____

"Happiness is a habit."

Things I'm proud of achieving today are...

_____

_____

_____

_____

_____

_____

_____

_____

_____

_____

_____

_____

_____

_____

_____

_____

"Believe. You're halfway there."

Things I feel today that I choose to release and leave here...

_____
_____
_____
_____
_____
_____
_____
_____
_____
_____
_____
_____
_____
_____
_____
_____
_____

"Believe. You're halfway there."

5 minute journaling

Date:

_____

_____

_____

_____

_____

_____

_____

_____

_____

_____

_____

_____

_____

_____

_____

_____

_____

_____

You Create
the Life
You Deserve

Morning Gratitude

Date: _____

Today I deserve to feel...

_____

_____

_____

Today I will give love to myself by...

_____

_____

_____

3 things I'm grateful for today are...

_____

_____

_____

"Happiness is a habit."

You are my

MAGIC

Things I'm proud of achieving today are...

_____
_____
_____
_____
_____
_____
_____
_____
_____
_____
_____
_____
_____
_____
_____
_____
_____
_____

"Believe. You're halfway there."

Things I feel today that I choose to release and leave here...

_____
_____
_____
_____
_____
_____
_____
_____
_____
_____
_____
_____
_____
_____
_____
_____

"Believe. You're halfway there."

5 minute journaling

Date:

_____

_____

_____

_____

_____

_____

_____

_____

_____

_____

_____

_____

_____

_____

_____

_____

_____

You Create
the Life
You Deserve

Morning Gratitude

Date: _____

Today I deserve to feel...

_____
_____
_____

Today I will give love to myself by...

_____
_____
_____

3 things I'm grateful for today are...

_____
_____
_____

"Happiness is a habit."

You are my MAGIC

Things I'm proud of achieving today are...

_____
_____
_____
_____
_____
_____
_____
_____
_____
_____
_____
_____
_____
_____
_____
_____

"Believe. You're halfway there."

Things I feel today that I choose
to release and leave here...

_____
_____
_____
_____
_____
_____
_____
_____
_____
_____
_____
_____
_____
_____
_____
_____

"Believe. You're halfway there."

5 minute journaling

Date:

_____

_____

_____

_____

_____

_____

_____

_____

_____

_____

_____

_____

_____

_____

_____

_____

_____

_____

You Create
the Life
You Deserve

Morning Gratitude

Date: _____

Today I deserve to feel...

_____
_____
_____

Today I will give love to myself by...

_____
_____
_____

3 things I'm grateful for today are...

_____
_____
_____

"Happiness is a habit."

You are my MAGIC

Things I'm proud of achieving today are...

_____
_____
_____
_____
_____
_____
_____
_____
_____
_____
_____
_____
_____
_____
_____
_____

"Believe. You're halfway there."

Things I feel today that I choose to release and leave here...

_____
_____
_____
_____
_____
_____
_____
_____
_____
_____
_____
_____
_____
_____
_____
_____
_____
_____

"Believe. You're halfway there."

5 minute journaling

Date:

_____

_____

_____

_____

_____

_____

_____

_____

_____

_____

_____

_____

_____

_____

_____

_____

_____

You Create
the Life
You Deserve

Morning Gratitude

Date: _____

Today I deserve to feel...

_____

_____

_____

Today I will give love to myself by...

_____

_____

_____

3 things I'm grateful for today are...

_____

_____

_____

"Happiness is a habit."

You are my MAGIC

Things I'm proud of achieving today are...

_____

_____

_____

_____

_____

_____

_____

_____

_____

_____

_____

_____

_____

_____

_____

"Believe. You're halfway there."

Things I feel today that I choose to release and leave here...

_____
_____
_____
_____
_____
_____
_____
_____
_____
_____
_____
_____
_____
_____
_____
_____
_____

"Believe. You're halfway there."

5 minute journaling

Date:

_____

_____

_____

_____

_____

_____

_____

_____

_____

_____

_____

_____

_____

_____

_____

_____

_____

You Create
the Life
You Deserve

Morning Gratitude

Date: _____

Today I deserve to feel...

_____
_____
_____

Today I will give love to myself by...

_____
_____
_____

3 things I'm grateful for today are...

_____
_____
_____

"Happiness is a habit."

You are my
MAGIC

Things I'm proud of achieving today are...

_____

_____

_____

_____

_____

_____

_____

_____

_____

_____

_____

_____

_____

_____

_____

_____

_____

_____

"Believe. You're halfway there."

Things I feel today that I choose to release and leave here...

_____
_____
_____
_____
_____
_____
_____
_____
_____
_____
_____
_____
_____
_____
_____
_____
_____

"Believe. You're halfway there."

5 minute journaling

Date:

_____

_____

_____

_____

_____

_____

_____

_____

_____

_____

_____

_____

_____

_____

_____

_____

_____

You Create
the Life
You Deserve

Morning Gratitude

Date: _____

Today I deserve to feel...

_____
_____
_____

Today I will give love to myself by...

_____
_____
_____

3 things I'm grateful for today are...

_____
_____
_____

"Happiness is a habit."

You are my MAGIC

Things I'm proud of achieving today are...

_____
_____
_____
_____
_____
_____
_____
_____
_____
_____
_____
_____
_____
_____
_____

"Believe. You're halfway there."

Things I feel today that I choose to release and leave here...

_____

_____

_____

_____

_____

_____

_____

_____

_____

_____

_____

_____

_____

_____

_____

_____

_____

"Believe. You're halfway there."

5 minute journaling

Date:

_____

_____

_____

_____

_____

_____

_____

_____

_____

_____

_____

_____

_____

_____

_____

_____

_____

_____

You Create
the Life
You Deserve

Morning Gratitude

Date: _____

Today I deserve to feel...

_____

_____

_____

Today I will give love to myself by...

_____

_____

_____

3 things I'm grateful for today are...

_____

_____

_____

"Happiness is a habit."

You are my MAGIC

Things I'm proud of achieving today are...

_____
_____
_____
_____
_____
_____
_____
_____
_____
_____
_____
_____
_____
_____
_____
_____
_____
_____

"Believe. You're halfway there."

Things I feel today that I choose to release and leave here...

_____

_____

_____

_____

_____

_____

_____

_____

_____

_____

_____

_____

_____

_____

_____

_____

_____

_____

_____

_____

"Believe. You're halfway there."

5 minute journaling   Date:

_____

_____

_____

_____

_____

_____

_____

_____

_____

_____

_____

_____

_____

_____

_____

_____

_____

_____

You Create
the Life
You Deserve

Morning Gratitude

Date: _____

Today I deserve to feel...

_____

_____

_____

Today I will give love to myself by...

_____

_____

_____

3 things I'm grateful for today are...

_____

_____

_____

"Happiness is a habit."

Things I'm proud of achieving today are...

_____
_____
_____
_____
_____
_____
_____
_____
_____
_____
_____
_____
_____
_____
_____
_____
_____

"Believe. You're halfway there."

Things I feel today that I choose to release and leave here...

_____

_____

_____

_____

_____

_____

_____

_____

_____

_____

_____

_____

_____

_____

_____

_____

_____

_____

"Believe. You're halfway there."

5 minute journaling   Date:

_____

_____

_____

_____

_____

_____

_____

_____

_____

_____

_____

_____

_____

_____

_____

_____

_____

_____

_____

You Create
the Life
You Deserve

Morning Gratitude

Date: _____

Today I deserve to feel...

_____

_____

_____

Today I will give love to myself by...

_____

_____

_____

3 things I'm grateful for today are...

_____

_____

_____

"Happiness is a habit."

You are my MAGIC

Things I'm proud of achieving today are...

_____

_____

_____

_____

_____

_____

_____

_____

_____

_____

_____

_____

_____

_____

_____

_____

"Believe. You're halfway there."

Things I feel today that I choose to release and leave here...

_____

_____

_____

_____

_____

_____

_____

_____

_____

_____

_____

_____

_____

_____

_____

_____

_____

"Believe. You're halfway there."

5 minute journaling

Date:

_____
_____
_____
_____
_____
_____
_____
_____
_____
_____
_____
_____
_____
_____
_____
_____
_____
_____
_____
_____
_____

*You Create
the Life
You Deserve*

Morning Gratitude

Date: _____

Today I deserve to feel...

_____

_____

_____

Today I will give love to myself by...

_____

_____

_____

3 things I'm grateful for today are...

_____

_____

_____

"Happiness is a habit."

You are my

MAGIC

Things I'm proud of achieving today are...

_____
_____
_____
_____
_____
_____
_____
_____
_____
_____
_____
_____
_____
_____
_____
_____

"Believe. You're halfway there."

Things I feel today that I choose to release and leave here...

_____

_____

_____

_____

_____

_____

_____

_____

_____

_____

_____

_____

_____

_____

_____

_____

"Believe. You're halfway there."

5 minute journaling

Date:

You Create
the Life
You Deserve

Morning Gratitude

Date: _____

Today I deserve to feel...

_____
_____
_____

Today I will give love to myself by...

_____
_____
_____

3 things I'm grateful for today are...

_____
_____
_____

"Happiness is a habit."

You are my
ARE MY
MAGIC

Things I'm proud of achieving today are...

_____
_____
_____
_____
_____
_____
_____
_____
_____
_____
_____
_____
_____
_____
_____
_____
_____

"Believe. You're halfway there."

Things I feel today that I choose to release and leave here...

_____
_____
_____
_____
_____
_____
_____
_____
_____
_____
_____
_____
_____
_____
_____
_____
_____

"Believe. You're halfway there."

5 minute journaling   ♥   Date:

_____

_____

_____

_____

_____

_____

_____

_____

_____

_____

_____

_____

_____

_____

_____

_____

_____

You Create
the Life
You Deserve

Morning Gratitude

Date: _____

Today I deserve to feel...

_____
_____
_____

Today I will give love to myself by...

_____
_____
_____

3 things I'm grateful for today are...

_____
_____
_____

"Happiness is a habit."

Things I'm proud of achieving today are...

_____
_____
_____
_____
_____
_____
_____
_____
_____
_____
_____
_____
_____
_____
_____
_____

"Believe. You're halfway there."

Things I feel today that I choose to release and leave here...

_____

_____

_____

_____

_____

_____

_____

_____

_____

_____

_____

_____

_____

_____

_____

_____

"Believe. You're halfway there."

5 minute journaling

Date:

Made in the USA
Coppell, TX
29 January 2023